Brain Waves

Ancient Egypt

Lynda Richardson
Phil Newton

Folens
Publishers

Contents

Editor: Joshua Dubin   Illustrator: Tony Dover
Cover design: Hybert Design and Type   Cover photograph: The Image Bank

First published 1995 by Folens Limited, Dunstable and Dublin.
Folens Limited, Albert House, Apex Business Centre, Boscombe Road, Dunstable LU5 4RL, England.
ISBN 1 85276-6603   Printed in Singapore by Craft Print.

Teachers' notes

Ancient Egypt
Observe the fertile strip along the Nile and consider reasons for the location of settlements along the river, both past and present. The children could locate their own country in relation to Egypt using a world map.

Time line
Encourage the children to add to the time line, such as other rulers and the spread of Christianity and Islam.

Foreign trade
The pharaoh and his officials traded products like grain and papyrus with other countries. Timber for boats came from Lebanon, while Nubia provided gold and animal skins for jewellery and clothing. Punt (Somalia) supplied elephant tusks for ornaments and cosmetic appliances, as well as horses for the pharaohs.

The army
Infantry soldiers, archers and chariot troops were recruited by scribes. The soldiers wore no protective armour, only linen kilts. They carried shields of ox hide, with copper- and bronze-headed weapons such as spears and axes. Bows were made of strips of wood, leather and horn.

Nile flooding
Divide the class into three groups and ask the children to enact the reactions of the farmers to too much, too little or adequate flooding. The teacher could act as a noble overseeing the workers in order to unobtrusively prompt the role-play.

Farming
Egyptian farmers grew flax for linen clothing and wheat, barley, beans, dates and figs for food. The children could consider the influence of location and climate on land use and discuss the kind of information they need before attempting the sheet on irrigation.

Irrigation
Irrigation involved a series of channels and dykes supplied with water by a hand-operated pump, a shaduf. Shadufs are still found in Egypt today but electric pumps are widespread. The building of the Aswan Dam in 1971 changed farming in Egypt by controlling the flow of water, allowing crops to be grown throughout the year.

Using the Nile
The Nile was the main highway for the transportation of people and goods, such as stone, statues, wood and cattle. Rich families made private journeys and hunted fish, hippopotamuses and birds. Today people cross the river to work, shop at markets, take tourists to the tombs and to visit family and friends. The Nile provides work for fishermen and tourist cruises. The children could use holiday snaps or brochures to investigate how Egypt's past influences its present.

The pyramids
The two methods of pyramid construction shown are:
● ascending ramps built around the four sides
● one ramp that ascends one face of the pyramid.
The children should recognise that lack of evidence means we do not know how the pyramids were built. They could develop and illustrate their own theories.

A mammoth task
The correct order is:
● finding North
● marking out four corners
● quarrying the stones
● taking stones to the Nile
● transporting the stones
● dragging the blocks into position
● fixing the casing of granite
● finished pyramid.
The Great Pyramid of Cheops would take modern builders the same time to build as the Egyptians: 15–20 years.

Tombs
The pyramids of the Old and Middle Kingdom kings were often robbed. In about 1550BC, pharaohs and nobles began to have tombs dug into the mountainside at Thebes (the Valley of the Kings).

Mummification
Natron (a salty substance from the banks of the Nile) preserved bodies more effectively than sand. One benefit of mummification was a well-preserved lifeform for the afterlife. The children could investigate the kind of evidence provided by an Egyptian mummy.

Temples
All temples had the same basic plan. The entrance was a gateway into one or more courtyards, behind which was a vast, painted hall (hypostyle) of columns. The sanctuary at the far end housed the divine statue.

Design a temple
The children could 'dedicate' their temple to a particular god, and include its statue (a card cut-out). Reference materials could include books, brochures and postcards.

Hierarchy
The statements should be matched as follows and placed in this hierarchical order:

Pharaoh	he or she was considered a god ...
High Priest	had great power ...
Nobles	were in charge of ...
Priests	looked after ...
Scribes	were state officials who ...
Craft workers	provided for the ...
Workers	did labouring jobs ...
Slaves	were owned by the rich ...

The children should understand hierarchy as graded importance in society. Extension activities could include investigation of particular groups of society.

Teachers' notes

Queen Hatshepsut
Consider how Tuthmosis III's desecration of Hatshepsut's wall paintings affects the evidence. More able children could discuss myths and legends as vehicles to perpetuate the beliefs of people in power.

Craft workers
The pictures depict:
- Sculptors completing a statue of Thutmose III. Inscriptions are chiselled on the back and painted.
- A cabinet-maker planing a chest. Two tools are shown: an adze (to shave wood) and a carpenter's square.
- A smith creating heat using a blowpipe and using tongs to hold small objects for soldering.
- A sandal-maker piercing the straps of a sandal.
- Jewellers, boring holes into stone beads with a bow drill and stringing the beads together.

Tools
The children could be shown the individual tools first (on separate sheets) and asked to make deductions about how they were used. The previous sheet could be used to help the children make valid deductions.

The law
The children could compare the modern justice system of their country today with that of Ancient Egypt. Perhaps discuss Ancient Athenian or Roman law and the absence of women from positions of authority.

The gods
The children could research other Egyptian gods and their roles and discuss current religious beliefs.

Popular religion
The ivory baton protected householders against snakes and scorpions. The cobra-goddess Meretseger was prayed to if workmen in the tombs were bitten or stung. Horus offered families protection from the Nile's crocodiles by standing on the crocodiles' backs.

Akhenaten
The High Priests were unhappy because they were no longer of importance: ceremonies to many gods would be unnecessary. The children could argue the priests' and the pharaoh's points of view.

The afterlife
Children could compare these objects with modern ones which serve the same purpose. The class could compile a fact file on the types of evidence available, such as wall paintings and hieroglyphs, and consider how and what they tell us about Ancient Egypt and the life of pharaohs.

Death mask
The children could look at death masks in books and photographs to help them create realistic designs. The masks could be mounted and displayed and observers invited to 'name the pharaoh'.

The weighing of the heart
The Egyptians believed that to join Osiris in the afterlife they had to pass certain tests. The virtuous would live a life more comfortable and prosperous than the one they had known in Egypt; the wicked suffered at the hands of the gods. This scene from *The Book of the Dead* depicts a dead man and his wife on trial before Osiris. Anubis weighs the man's heart against the feather of truth: equal weight means he has been virtuous, but the monster will eat him if his heart weighs more than the feather. Thoth, scribe of the gods, records the verdict.

Buried treasure
The objects were all found in tombs. Clockwise:
- Canopic jar – used to store internal organs.
- The Eye of Horus – the Egyptians believed that it watched over and protected the pharaoh.
- The scarab beetle – a lucky charm or amulet.
- The cobra – a goddess who destroyed enemies by spitting at them.
- The double crown – a symbol of rule over Upper and Lower Egypt.
- Sceptre and flail – symbols of the afterlife.

A family outing 1
This page shows a wall-painting (about 1425BC) from the tomb of Nakht. A cat in the rushes and a goose on each papyrus skiff were once visible but have been destroyed. Nakht was probably spearing fish (on the right-hand side); the artist has omitted the spear. For outdoor entertainment men fished with spears, fowled with throwing sticks and hunted wild animals (hyenas and gazelles) with arrows, from light chariots.

A family outing 2
The children could compare Ancient Egyptian leisure with today's leisure pursuits and those of other historical periods (such as Roman gladiators or modern fox-hunting). The children could consider sports which involve animals, or compile a guide to the leisure pursuits of different historical periods.

Making music
The picture dates from about 1425BC. One musician plays a double flute and another a standing harp with a soundbox covered by a leopard skin. The woman in the centre is playing a long-necked stringed instrument, perhaps a lute. The children could compare these instruments with similar ones used today.

Make-up and jewellery
The children could add features they have discovered from reference books. The model could be decorated to depict (for example) a pharaoh, a child or a slave. The children could design their own jewellery. Discuss the use of jewellery and other aspects of personal appearance, as a status symbol. For example, Britain's monarch sometimes wears a crown; wealthy Roman women wore rings, necklaces, ear-rings and brooches.

Teachers' notes

Children's games
Each of the two players of Senet had counters, either conical or barrel-shaped, which they had to move along the outer lines to reach the end of the centre line before their opponent. Counters were moved after each throw of a 'throwstick' (die). The board also had advantage and forfeit squares. Encourage the children to describe how games have changed, such as with new technology.

Papyrus
Scribes wrote on scrolls made from papyrus reeds which grew along the banks of the Nile. The reeds were cut, the outer rind peeled away and the stems cut into strips and soaked in water. The strips were woven together vertically and horizontally, covered with a cloth and pounded to release the sap, which bound them into a sheet. The sheets were then joined to make a scroll.

Hieroglyphs 1 and 2
In the earliest hieroglyphs, pictures simply represented objects. As the system evolved, pictures and signs came to represent individual letters or groups of letters (up to five). Sometimes at the end of a word there was a picture to clarify its meaning. The children could use reference books to find out where cartouches were used (such as monuments, columns, wall-paintings). Empty cartouches are often found; the children could try to deduce why. (Pharaohs often died before tombs or temples were completed.)

Number
The children could set problems for other members of the class, based on everyday Ancient Egyptian situations, such as taxation and construction of pyramids.
The answers to the Egyptian sums are:
- Rahotep saw 326 animals.
- The farmer bought 1 061 animals.
- Rahotep has counted 101 036 stones.

The answers to the translations are:

$$||| \ ||| \ | \ + \ ||| \qquad = \cap$$

$$||| \ ||| \ + \ || \qquad = \ ||| \ ||| \ ||$$

$$\cap \cap \ ||| \ + \ \cap \ | \qquad = \cap \cap \cap \ ||| \ |$$

$$\cap \cap \cap \ ||| \ ||| \ | \ + \ \cap \ ||| \ ||| \ || \ = \cap \cap \cap \cap \cap \ ||| \ ||$$

$$\wp \ + \ \cap \cap \cap \ ||| \ | \ = \wp \cap \cap \cap \ ||| \ |$$

$$\wp \wp \ ||| \ || \ + \ \cap \ ||| \ = \wp \wp \ \cap \ ||| \ ||| \ ||$$

$$\underset{\sim}{\xi} \ + \ \wp \wp \ \cap \ | \ = \ \underset{\sim}{\xi} \ \wp \wp \ \cap \ |$$

Homes 1
To make their homes the Egyptians took mud from the banks of the Nile, mixed it with straw, placed it in a wooden mould and baked it in the sun. The same method is used today. The children could investigate the homes of wealthy Ancient Egyptians and write an estate agent's report on the house they have researched.

Homes 2
The children should understand the influence of climate on structural design. For example, small windows with shutters eliminate light and allow breezes. Glass windows are rare because they allow light in and they cost more.

Clues from the past
Make separate enlarged photocopies of each object. Ask the children to deduce what the items might be. The objects are: mirror, sandals, headrest/pillow, whisk, sieve.

Time detectives
The Egyptian kitchen utensils are a whisk and a sieve, both made of wicker. The cosmetic mirror is made of polished bronze with a wooden papyrus-design handle. The sandals were hand-made from leather or reed. The headrest, used on beds, was made of alabaster or wood.

Tutankhamun: fact or point of view?
The children could list both facts and points of view about themselves to discuss with the class, to ensure that the whole class understands the difference. After completing the worksheet, the children could guess who might have made some of the statements.

Tutankhamun: read all about it!
The children should imagine they are actually at the scene of the discovery with Howard Carter, Harry Burton (photographer), Arthur C Mace (archaeologist), Lindsley F Hall and Walter Hauser (draughtsmen). They could consider (in interviews) the roles of the people involved:
- drawing a plan of the tomb, including scale drawings of the artefacts in their positions
- compiling a photographic record of all the artefacts
- cataloguing, repairing and restoring the artefacts.

The children could collect evidence about the artefacts for their articles.

Legacy wordsearch
The children could look, for example, at:
- Astronomy – how is this used today? One example is horoscopes: the children could identify their own star sign and write a personality profile.
- Papyrus – how is paper made today? The children could identify differences and similarities between past and present.

Ancient Egyptian anagrams
The answers are:
1. Nefertiti
2. obelisk
3. Amun
4. Anubis
5. Eye of Horus
6. Canopic jar
7. pyramids
8. Rosetta stone
9. Cleopatra
10. Sphinx.

The children could devise and solve their own Ancient Egyptian anagrams.

Ancient Egypt

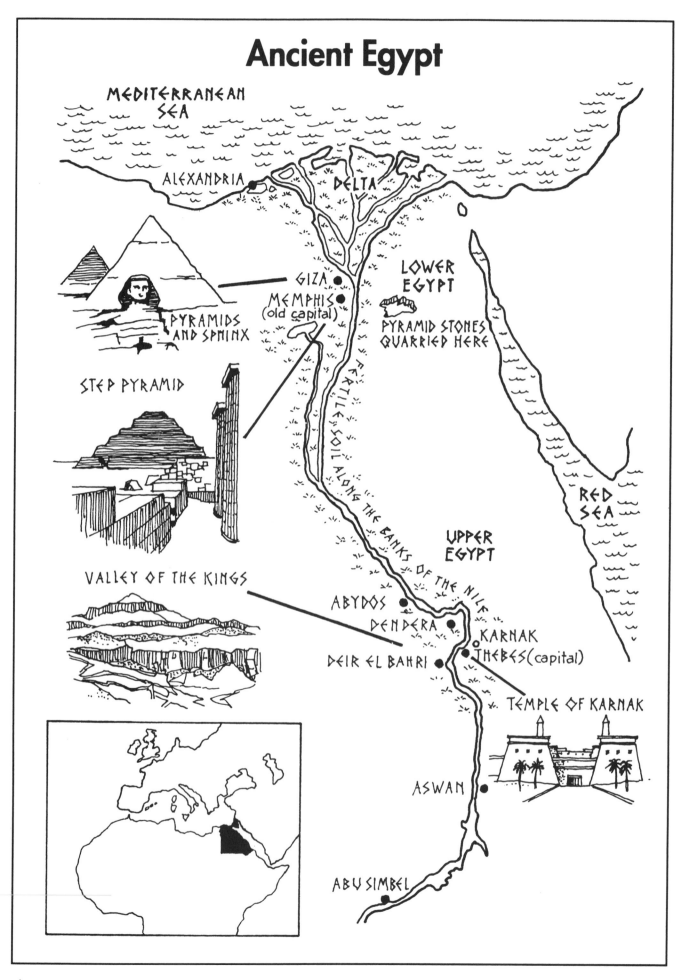

MEDITERRANEAN SEA

ALEXANDRIA

DELTA

LOWER EGYPT

GIZA

MEMPHIS (old capital)

PYRAMID STONES QUARRIED HERE

PYRAMIDS AND SPHINX

STEP PYRAMID

FERTILE SOIL ALONG THE BANKS OF THE NILE

RED SEA

UPPER EGYPT

VALLEY OF THE KINGS

ABYDOS

DENDERA

KARNAK

THEBES (capital)

DEIR EL BAHRI

TEMPLE OF KARNAK

ASWAN

ABU SIMBEL

Brain Waves: Ancient Egypt

Time line

3000BC

Writing and hieroglyphs are developed.

King Menes, first ruler of Egypt.

The age of the pyramids and the Sphinx.

2500BC

THE OLD KINGDOM

2200BC Egypt divided.

2040BC King Mentuhotep unites Egypt. THE MIDDLE KINGDOM

1640BC Chariots are introduced.

Pharaohs are buried in tombs cut into the rock at the Valley of the Kings.

1570BC A time of great wealth and splendour.

Karnak Temple

Egypt defeats its enemies.

1570BC – 1342BC
Some rulers of Egypt are:
Hatshepsut
Akhenaten
Tutankhamun

THE NEW KINGDOM

1070BC Egypt is invaded and conquered by the Nubians, Assyrians, Persians and Greeks.

Cleopatra: the last Queen of Egypt.

Alexander the Great 332 B.C

30BC Egypt becomes part of the Roman Empire.

THE LATE PERIOD

Foreign trade

- The Ancient Egyptians traded their goods by bartering, which is exchanging goods for other goods of equal value. Why do you think they traded with other countries?

- Can you match the imports in the boats below with the uses the Ancient Egyptians put them to?

Imports:

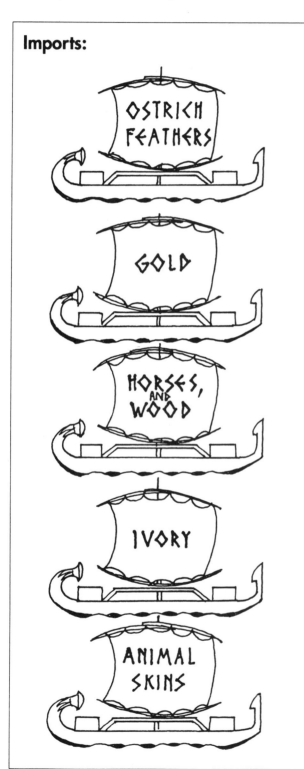

Used for:

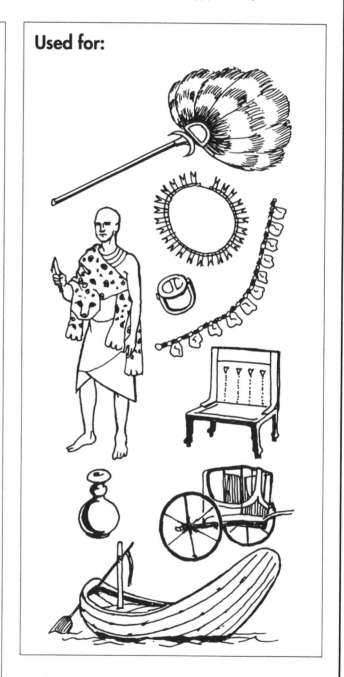

In about 400 BC Egyptians started to use coins as money.
- Give one reason why they did this.
- Find out what the coins looked like.
- Are they the same as coins today?

The army

● Here are three soldiers from different times in history. Put them in the correct order.

● Describe how arms and armour have changed through history.

_____

_____

_____

_____

_____

_____

_____

_____

● Find out more about the Ancient Egyptian army.
  Use library books to help you.

Nile flooding

Every year the River Nile flooded its banks.
The Ancient Egyptians thought this was caused by the gods.
The three pictures below show what could happen when the Nile flooded.
The speech bubbles contain causes and consequences of these types of floods.

● Match the words with the floods by drawing the correct faces from the pictures
next to each bubble.

● How do you think flooding is controlled in Egypt today?

Farming

Historians are like detectives. They gather as much evidence as they can to find out about the past.

This is an artist's impression of a wall painting in the tomb of Menna, who was a noble in the Ancient Egyptian capital of Thebes.

● Use this picture to answer the following questions.

1. How was the land around the river (the Nile) used?

2. Which animals are used in farming?

3. What tools are the farmers using to help them work the land?

4. How do they sow seeds for new crops?

5. How do they make sure the seeds are firmly trodden down?

6. How are crops harvested?

7. How do you think the Egyptians watered their crops?

Irrigation

Farming on the Nile with a shaduf

● Identify the methods that the farmers are using in this picture.

_____

_____

_____

_____

● How do you think new technology affects Egyptian farmers today?

_____

_____

_____

_____

Using the Nile

Egyptian farmers have always depended on the Nile, but it has other uses too.
Here are some examples.

- Explain to a friend how using the Nile has changed or stayed the same.

- Why do you think people both past and present need to travel across or along the Nile? Discuss this in small groups.

Brain Waves: Ancient Egypt

The pyramids

The Great Pyramid of Cheops is 146m high and each side measures 230m. It is made from more than two million blocks of stone – enough to build a wall around the world.

● How did the Egyptians move the stones?
● How did they lift the stones without pulleys and cranes?

The pictures show two methods of building a pyramid.

● What is the difference between the two methods?

_____
_____
_____
_____
_____
_____
_____

● Look at books about Ancient Egypt. Why do people have different ideas about how the pyramids were built?

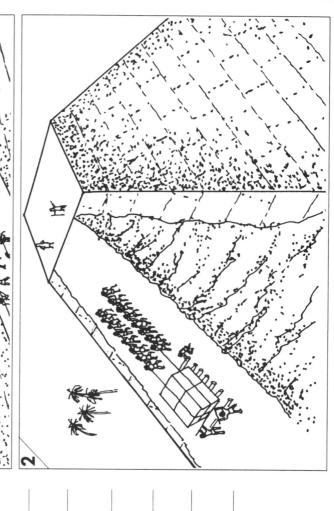

1

2

A mammoth task

Imagine you are the Great Chief of Works in charge of building a pharaoh's pyramid.
● Cut out the tasks below and arrange them in order. Present your plan to the pharaoh.

Taking stones to the Nile

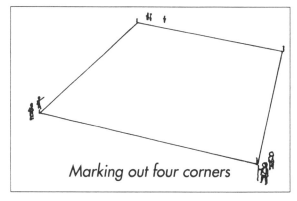

Marking out four corners

Finding North

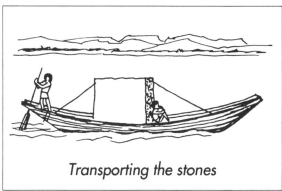

Transporting the stones

Dragging the blocks into position

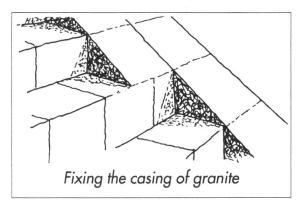

Fixing the casing of granite

Quarrying the stones

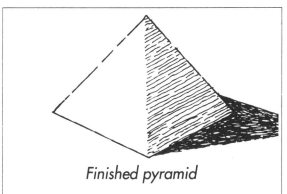

Finished pyramid

Tombs

Early Egyptians built pyramids to bury their pharaohs.
Later, they built tombs for pharaohs in the rock walls of the Valleys of
the Kings and Queens at Thebes.

● Why do you think they did this instead of building pyramids?

_____

_____

_____

_____

Tombs have given us a great deal of information about the lives of the Ancient Egyptians.

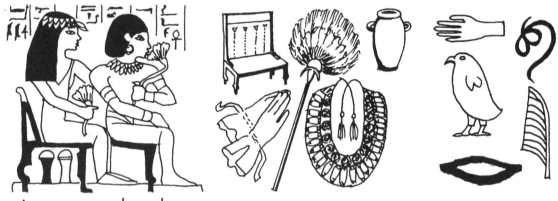

● Imagine you are a pharaoh.
  What things would you have buried with you in your tomb and why?

_____

_____

_____

_____

_____

● Paint some pictures and patterns to decorate your tomb.
  Remember that Ancient Egyptian tombs are often painted with scenes of everyday life.

Mummification

Wealthy Egyptians were mummified after death. This means their bodies were preserved. They thought that their bodies would be needed in the afterlife.

● Match the pictures with the descriptions. Cut them out and put them in the correct order.

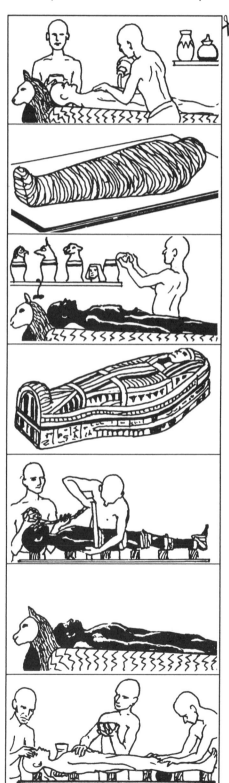

Rub the body with natron to dry and preserve the skin. Leave for 40 days.
Rub cream, oil and perfume all over the body.
Cover the body with thick sticky resin that will harden when it dries.
Tie up the body with fresh, knotted reeds and ropes.
Remove the brain with a hook through the nose and take out the internal organs. Place them in canopic jars.
Wrap the body in fresh linen bandages from head to foot.
Place the body in a coffin, ready for the funeral.

Brain Waves: Ancient Egypt

Temples

Architecture is the way a building is designed and built, including its shape, size and features. Look at these examples of Ancient Egyptian architecture.

Luxor Temple

Ptah and Hathor Temple, Philae

Isis Temple, Philae

● Choose one of these buildings and describe it.

_____

_____

_____

_____

_____

● Why do you think the Ancient Egyptians built their temples in such grand styles?

Brain Waves: Ancient Egypt   © Folens

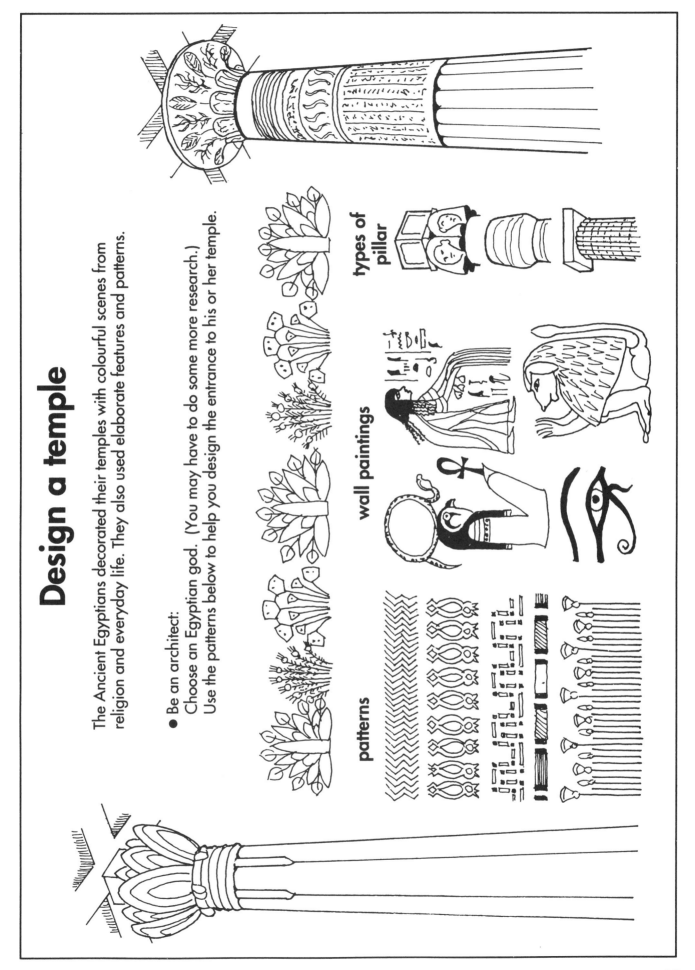

Design a temple

The Ancient Egyptians decorated their temples with colourful scenes from religion and everyday life. They also used elaborate features and patterns.

● Be an architect:
Choose an Egyptian god. (You may have to do some more research.) Use the patterns below to help you design the entrance to his or her temple.

types of pillar

wall paintings

patterns

Hierarchy

- Match the people in the pictures below with their descriptions.
- Arrange them in order of their importance in Ancient Egyptian society.

Priests

Craft workers

Scribes

Workers

Pharaoh

High Priest

Slaves

Nobles

He had great power and looked after money received from the temple lands. He was the only person who could open a sacred shrine where a statue of a god was kept.	He or she was considered to be a god by the Ancient Egyptians and had supreme power. He or she was a warrior.
They provided for the needs of the wealthy. They included potters, carpenters, stonemasons, jewellers, metal workers, bronzesmiths, cobblers and artists.	They did labouring jobs, such as working on the farms or in the homes of the rich people.
They looked after the temples and estates of the gods and goddesses.	They were in charge of the pharaoh's land, lived in large houses and enjoyed banquets, hunting and fishing. They had servants.
They were owned by rich Egyptians to work in their homes and on the land. Some, if they were lucky, could win their freedom.	They were state officials who wrote about medicine, mathematics and astronomy. They also collected taxes.

Brain Waves: Ancient Egypt

© Folens

Queen Hatshepsut

Sometimes people tell stories to explain the past.
Here are two different stories that both tell how Queen Hatshepsut became a pharaoh.

1 From the wall of the temple of Queen Hatshepsut at Deir-el-Bahri:

Amen-Ra, King of Gods, wanted to create a great queen to rule Egypt. Isis said: "If you create such a queen, my blessing and wisdom shall be upon her." Then Thoth suggested Ahmes, wife of the Pharaoh Thutmose, to be the mother of this great queen when their baby, Hatshepsut, was born. Amen-Ra blessed the baby, taking her up in his arms and giving her the kiss of power, so that she might indeed become a great queen.

2 Some history books say that Queen Hatshepsut ruled on behalf of her stepson, Thutmose, who was too young to rule on his own. She decided to take over the government of Egypt completely and was pharaoh for 20 years.
When her stepson later came to the throne, as King Tuthmosis III, he had her name and image removed from buildings and records. He believed that she had had no right to the throne.

Queen Hatshepsut's temple

- Why do you think there are two different versions of the story that tell how Hatshepsut became Queen?
- Why do you think Hatshepsut wrote the story on the walls of her temple?
- Which story do you believe?

Craft workers

Here is some evidence from wall paintings.
The pictures show craft workers in the workshops of the temple at Karnak.

● Look at the pictures. What do you think the craft workers are making?

_____

_____

_____

● What names would we give their jobs today?

_____

_____

_____

● How have the jobs changed or stayed the same? Think about tools and materials.

_____

_____

Brain Waves: Ancient Egypt

Tools

Look at these pictures of tools that the Ancient Egyptians used and tools that we use today.

Then

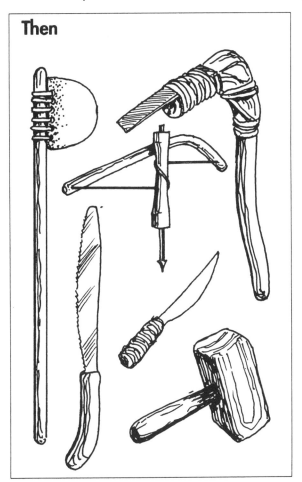

Now

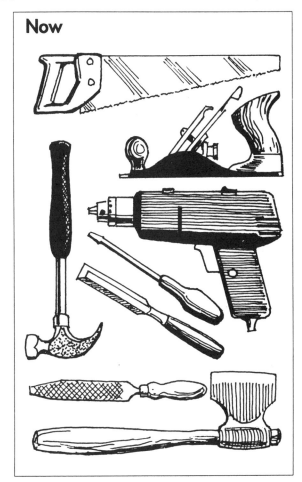

● What do you think the Egyptian tools were used for?

_____

_____

_____

_____

● Choose one of the Egyptian tools and compare it with a modern tool.
  What are the differences between the tools? Is anything the same?

_____

_____

_____

The law

Criminals in Ancient Egypt were tried in local courts by a group of judges.
These were important local men.
Punishments for criminals who were found guilty included beating,
hard labour and the loss of an ear or nose.
Witnesses had to swear by Amun and the pharaoh to tell the truth.

- Imagine that you have been
  accused of robbing a royal tomb.
  You could face the death penalty.

- Prepare a speech for your trial,
  giving details of where you were
  and what you were doing when the
  robbery took place.
  Remember – your life depends on it!

I swear by Amun and the pharoah that the following statement is true ...

seal

The gods

Thoth	Osiris	Isis
Moon god, inventor of writing.	God of the dead.	Goddess, protector of women.

● Why do you think the Egyptians might have prayed to these gods?

Thoth _____

_____

_____

_____

_____

Osiris _____

_____

_____

_____

_____

Isis _____

_____

_____

_____

_____

● Imagine that you are an Ancient Egyptian child.
  What might you have asked the gods for help with?

Make up a name for your god.

_____

_____

_____

_____

_____

● Find some examples of Ancient Egyptian gods to whom Egyptian children
  might have prayed.

Popular religion

Most Ancient Egyptians worshipped gods and goddesses who could help them in their daily lives. They also believed that jewellery and amulets (lucky charms) gave them protection.

This magical baton was made from ivory and was used to draw a circle around a house to protect it.

- Look at the picture carefully. What do you think it protected the house from?

_____

_____

_____

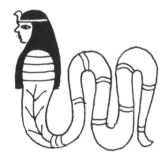

Meretseger

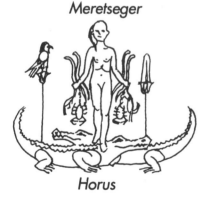

Horus

- Why do you think the workmen who built the tombs may have prayed to Meretseger?

_____

_____

_____

- This is the god Horus. What do you think families asked him for protection from?

_____

_____

_____

- Do you know of any lucky charms people keep today? Write a list.

_____

_____

_____

_____

Brain Waves: Ancient Egypt

Akhenaten

Pharaoh Akhenaten ruled Ancient Egypt from 1372BC to 1354BC. He wanted people to worship only one god, the Sun, instead of many different gods.

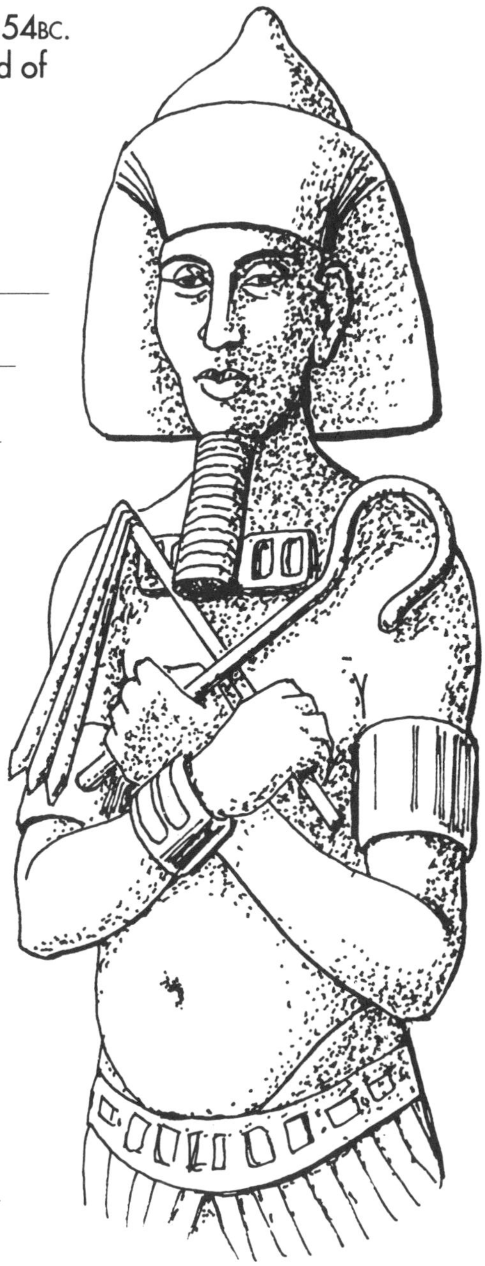

● If you were a ruler in your country, what changes would you make? Why?

_____

_____

_____

_____

_____

_____

_____

_____

_____

_____

● Why do you think the high priests were unhappy about Akhenaten's ideas?

_____

_____

_____

_____

_____

The afterlife

● Look at the evidence below. These objects are being taken to the pharaoh's tomb. What are the objects? What were they used for?

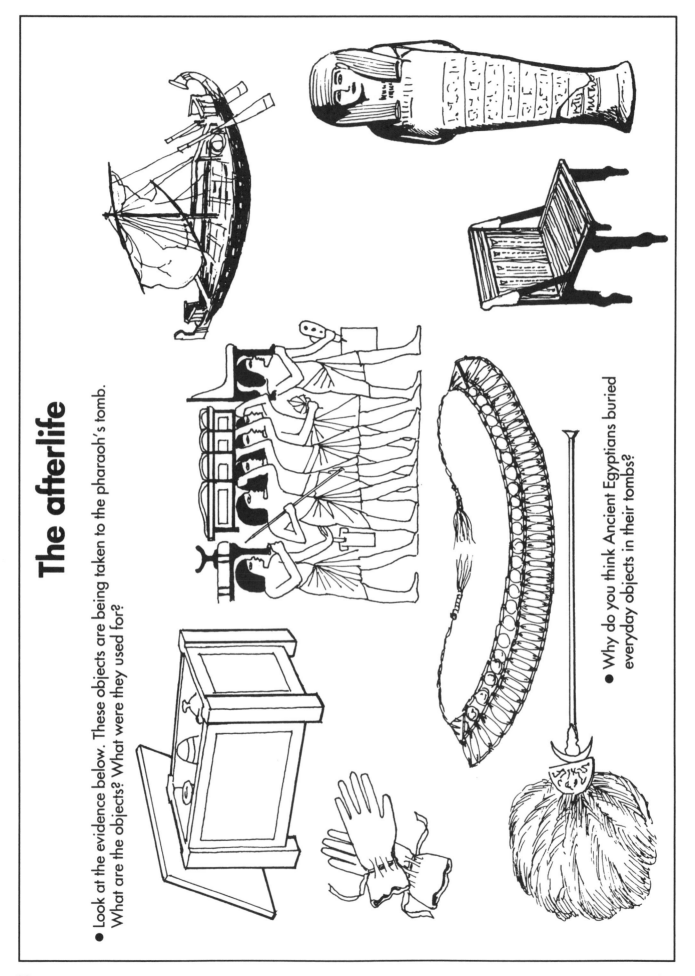

● Why do you think Ancient Egyptians buried everyday objects in their tombs?

Brain Waves: Ancient Egypt

Death mask

● Imagine you are a pharaoh. Design your own death mask.

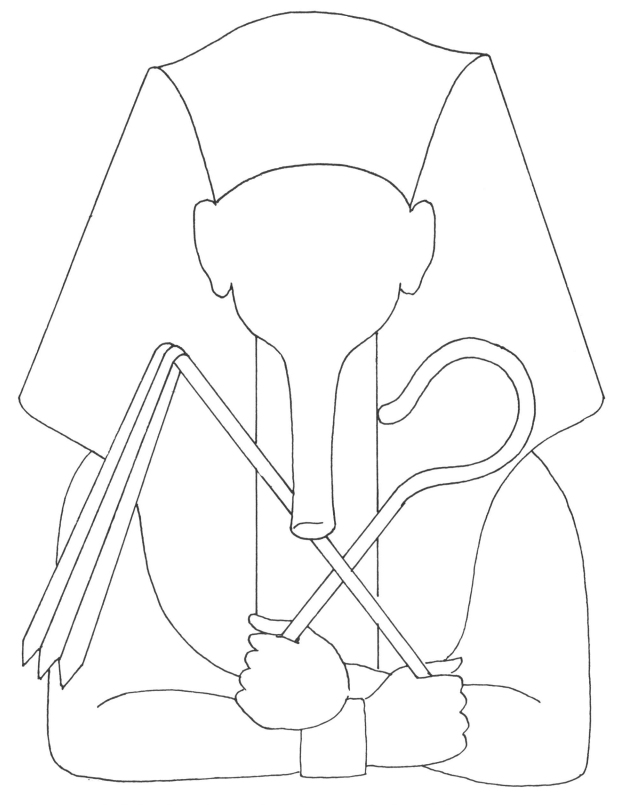

● Why do you think the pharaohs were buried wearing death masks?

The weighing of the heart

● Why do you think the Ancient Egyptians believed that the gods weighed the dead pharaoh's heart?

_____

_____

● Find out who the gods in the picture are and what they did.

_____

_____

● How would you find out if someone had been a good or bad person in their life?

_____

_____

● Make a list of your own good points and things you could improve about yourself. Think about: your personality, friends, school work, home life, and so on.

Good points _____	Things I can improve _____
_____	_____
_____	_____
_____	_____
_____	_____

Buried treasure

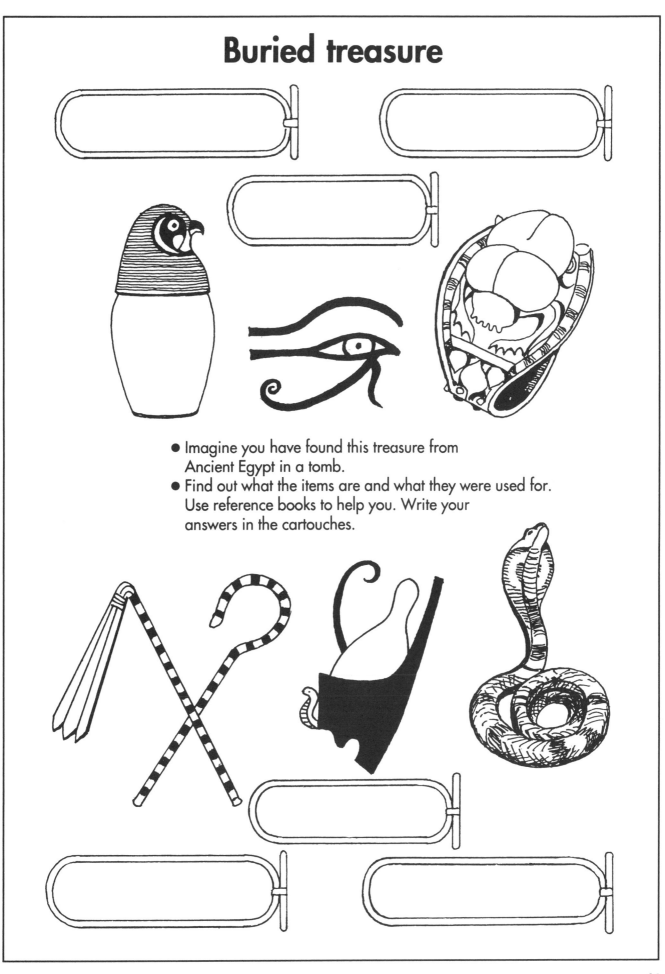

- Imagine you have found this treasure from Ancient Egypt in a tomb.
- Find out what the items are and what they were used for. Use reference books to help you. Write your answers in the cartouches.

Brain Waves: Ancient Egypt

A family outing 1

A wall painting from the tomb of Nakht (about 1425 BC).

A family outing 2

Nakht was a royal scribe. Look at the picture of a wall painting from his tomb. Be a time detective and answer these questions about the evidence.

● How many people can you see in the picture? _____

● Who do you think they are? _____
_____
_____

● Why do you think each person is there? _____
_____
_____

● The artist has drawn Nakht twice in the same picture.
  Why? What is Nakht doing each time?
_____
_____
_____

● On the right of the picture, the artist has left something out.
  Look at Nakht's hands. What do you think Nakht would have been holding?
_____
_____

● Look at the women and the children. Why do you think they are drawn
  much smaller than men? What are they doing?
_____
_____

● What does the evidence tell us about the clothes that people wore in Ancient Egypt?
_____
_____

Making music

Here is a picture of part of a wall painting (about 1425BC) that shows a feast in the home of Nakht, a royal scribe. It comes from Nakht's tomb.

- Choose a time detective from your class. Make up some questions about this picture for them to answer.
  Choose your questions to help them look carefully at the evidence.
  Here are some words to help you plan your questions:

why   how   clothes   sounds   instruments

My questions are _____

_____

_____

_____

(Continue over the page.)

- How could the time detective find the answers to your questions?

Make-up and jewellery

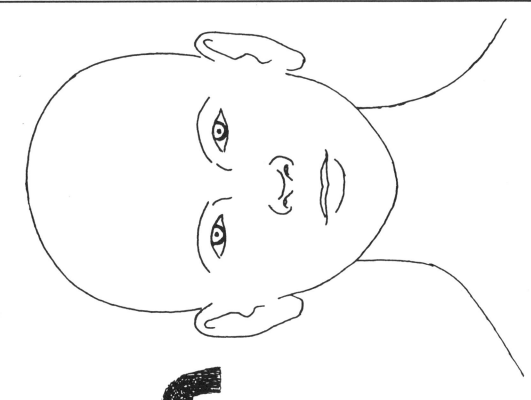

Ancient Egyptians, especially the wealthy, enjoyed wearing make-up and jewellery for feasts and celebrations. They even rubbed gazelle dung and hippopotamus fat into their scalps to prevent baldness.

● Use the information below to prepare this person for the evening feast.

– Around their eyes they used black eye-liner made from lead ore.

– Black wigs, made from human hair, were worn as status symbols.

– Jewels were made from gold and semi-precious stones.

– Red lip-paint was made from ochre and henna.

– A cone made from animal fat and the scent of lotus or lily was attached to the top of the wig. This slowly melted over the hair.

– Lotus flowers were used as popular designs for necklaces and bracelets.

– Blue eye-shadow was made from copper ore.

● Use other sources to make your model as accurate as possible.

Children's games

Ancient Egyptian children enjoyed playing games, including leap-frog, ball-catching and playing with dolls.

Children also played board games.
This game is called *Senet*.

● How do you think it was played?
● Does it look like any of your games?

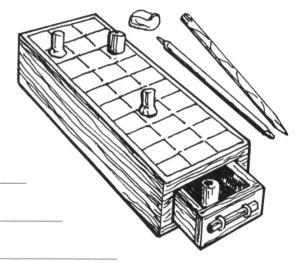

_____

_____

_____

_____

_____

● Write a list of the games you play with your friends.

Indoor games _____

Outdoor games _____

● What is the most popular game in your class?
● Have games changed or stayed the same since Ancient Egyptian times?

Papyrus

- Look at the pictures below.
- Cut them out and stick them on paper.
- Use them to describe how the Ancient Egyptians made paper from the papyrus plant.

- Look at the pictures of four pens below.
- Cut them out. Arrange them in order, from the earliest to the most recent.

- Describe how pens have changed over time.

Hieroglyphs 1

In 1799 a soldier in Napoleon's army found a stone at Rosetta, in Egypt.
On it was one inscription, written three times: in Greek, in demotic and in hieratic (early forms of writing).
Scholars who could read Greek were able to work out, for the first time, how to read hieroglyphs.

This is the hieroglyphic alphabet:

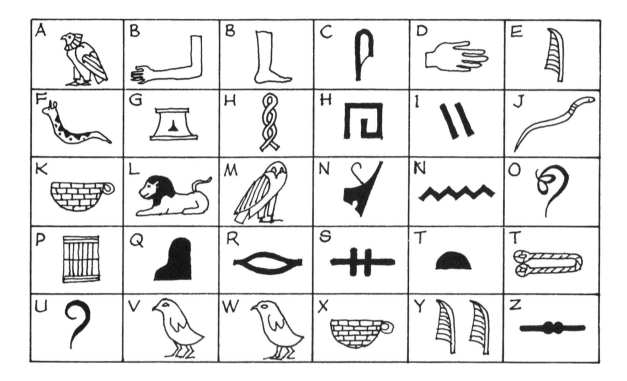

Hieroglyphs encased in an oval cartouche spelled the names of pharaohs.

● Why do you think Ancient Egyptians used cartouches?
● Look at the cartouches below. To which pharaohs do they belong?

1   2   3

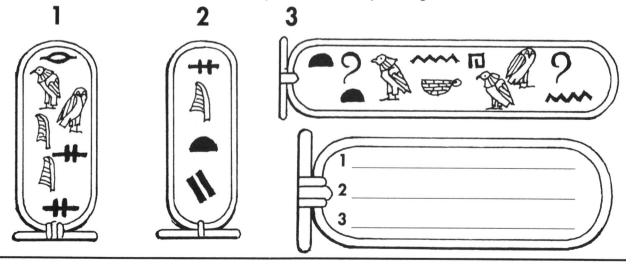

Brain Waves: Ancient Egypt

Hieroglyphs 2

- Design a cartouche for your own name using the hieroglyph alphabet.

- Remember that the Ancient Egyptians sometimes wrote in different directions.

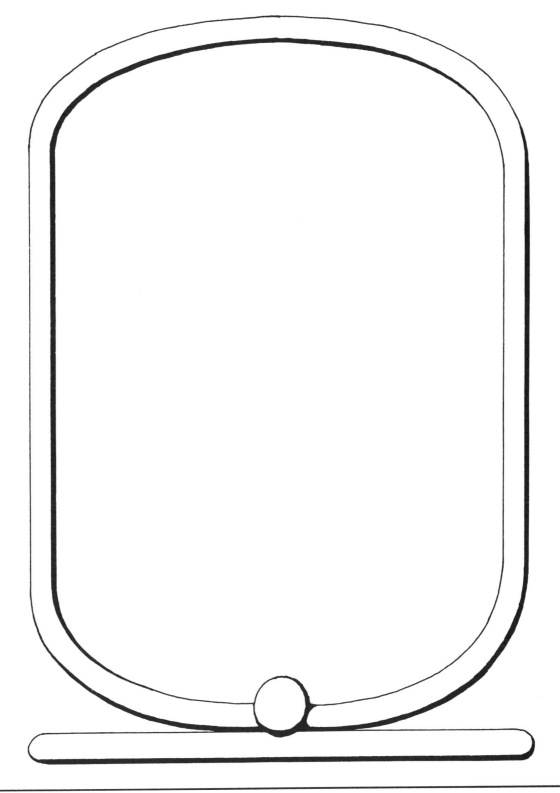

Number

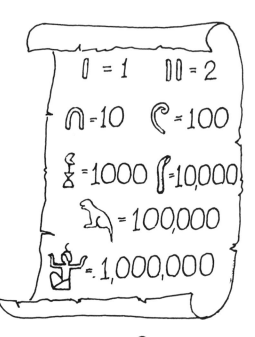

Scribes used these numbers to do calculations for everyday situations, for example how to divide rations of food among workers, or how to measure the size of a field.

- Help Rahotep, the Royal Scribe, to solve these problems.

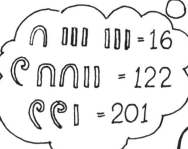

- If Rahotep saw  sheep, ⎯ oxen and ⎯ goats in one field, how many animals did he see?

- If a farmer bought ⎯ sheep and ⎯ goats, how many animals would he have altogether?

The pharaoh has asked Rahotep how many stones will be in the new temple.
- How many stones has Rahotep counted altogether?

Rahotep has found some numbers that he does not understand.
- Find the answers and translate them into Ancient Egyptian for him.

7 +3	6 +2	23 +11	37 +18	100 +34	205 +13	1000 +211

40

Brain Waves: Ancient Egypt

© Folens

Homes 1

Most homes and ordinary buildings in Ancient Egypt were built from clay bricks.
Here are some models of Ancient Egyptian homes that were found in tombs.

- Most of Egypt is desert. Where do you think the Ancient Egyptians found the mud to make bricks?

- Why do you think the houses had flat roofs and small windows?

- Think of the advantages and disadvantages of making houses from mud bricks.

- Could you have mud brick houses where you live?

- Why do you think no Ancient Egyptian houses survive for us to look at today?

- Why do you think the Ancient Egyptians built their temples and pyramids from stone?

Homes 2

Here are some examples of Egyptian homes today.

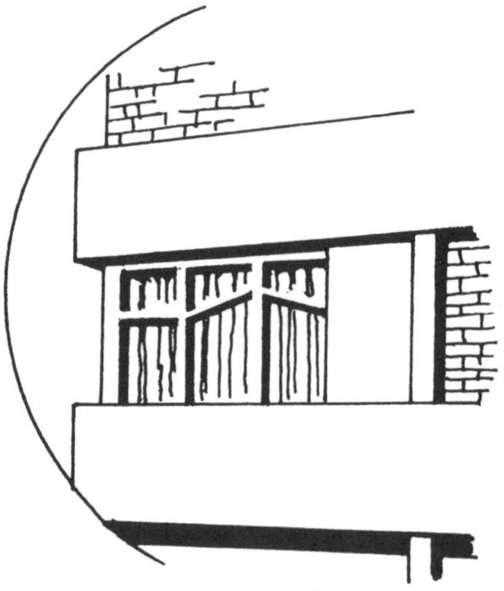

- Write down the differences between homes in Ancient Egypt and those in Egypt today. Think about windows, materials, shape and design.

_____

_____

_____

_____

- How have Egyptian homes changed or stayed the same?

_____

_____

_____

_____

- Find out if mud bricks are made in the same way today as they were in Ancient Egypt.

Brain Waves: Ancient Egypt

Clues from the past

Howard Carter could not believe his eyes when he discovered treasure in King Tutankhamun's tomb on 26 November 1922.

● Match the treasured objects from Ancient Egypt with the objects on the right that do the same job today.

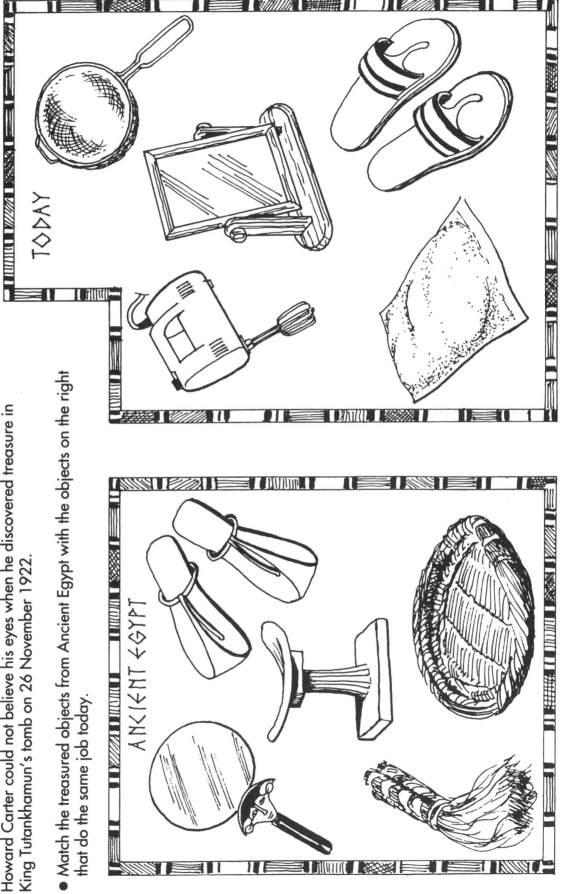

TODAY

ANCIENT EGYPT

Brain Waves: Ancient Egypt

Time detectives

● How have these objects changed?
  Think about shape, size, materials and design.

Object	Ancient Egypt	Today		

Mirror:

Sandals:

Sieve:

Headrest:

Whisk:

Tutankhamun: fact or point of view?

- Read the statements below. Do you think they are facts or points of view?
- Write **F** for a fact or **P** for a point of view. One has been done for you.

1 The tomb of Tutankhamun was discovered by Howard Carter in November 1922. ___F___

2 King Tutankhamun's tomb should have been left the way it was found. _____

3 Tutankhamun's treasure should stay in Egyptian museums. _____

4 Tutankhamun's tomb was found in the Valley of the Kings at Thebes. _____

5 The face of his mummy was covered with a golden mask. _____

6 Tutankhamun should not have been buried with so much treasure. _____

7 No other pharaoh's tomb was found to contain as much treasure as that of Tutankhamun. _____

8 Nothing of such great wonder will ever be discovered again. _____

9 One of the pieces of treasure was the most beautiful monument in the world. _____

10 Inside the stone sarcophagus were three coffins. The third was almost 2 metres long and made of solid gold. _____

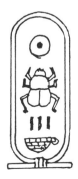

Tutankhamun: read all about it!

When Howard Carter discovered the tomb of Tutankhamun, his friend Lord Carnarvon asked him: "Can you see anything?" Carter replied: "Yes, wonderful things."

- Find out about the objects found in the tomb.
- Imagine you are a newspaper reporter writing about this great discovery. Write your article for *The Daily Blurb*.

The Daily Blurb

22nd. November 1922   Price 1d.

Legacy wordsearch

The Ancient Egyptians passed on ideas and knowledge which affect our lives today. This information survived because the Egyptians wrote it down.

- The words in this wordsearch show some of the ideas they gave us.
- Try to find all of the words.

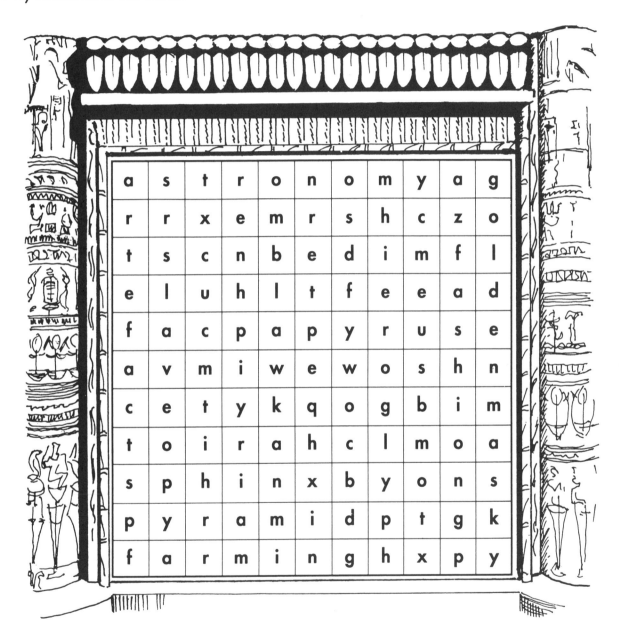

a	s	t	r	o	n	o	m	y	a	g
r	r	x	e	m	r	s	h	c	z	o
t	s	c	n	b	e	d	i	m	f	l
e	l	u	h	l	t	f	e	e	a	d
f	a	c	p	a	p	y	r	u	s	e
a	v	m	i	w	e	w	o	s	h	n
c	e	t	y	k	q	o	g	b	i	m
t	o	i	r	a	h	c	l	m	o	a
s	p	h	i	n	x	b	y	o	n	s
p	y	r	a	m	i	d	p	t	g	k
f	a	r	m	i	n	g	h	x	p	y

tombs	papyrus	slave	artefacts
pyramid	chariot	temples	astronomy
sphinx	archaeology	law	hieroglyph
farming	golden mask	fashion	

Ancient Egyptian anagrams

● Unjumble the letters to find the names of these Ancient Egyptian people
and objects and write them in the box provided. Use reference books to help you.

1 e e i f t r i N t

2 l i o s b k e

3 n A u m

4 u n s i A b

5 E e y f o o s H r u

6 a C p c i o n a r j

7 y m r i p a s d

8 e s t o a t R t e n o s

9 a l e C t a r p o

10 h n i s x p

1	_____	6	_____
2	_____	7	_____
3	_____	8	_____
4	_____	9	_____
5	_____	10	_____

Brain Waves: Ancient Egypt